Hello, David

A STUDY OF A SCHOOL NEIGHBORHOOD

by PAUL R. HANNA *and* GENEVIEVE ANDERSON HOYT

WILLIAM S. GRAY, *Reading Director*

Illustrated by Eleanor Campbell, Walter Oschman,
and John Osebold

THE SOCIAL STUDIES PROGRAM
CURRICULUM FOUNDATION SERIES
REG. U.S. PAT. OFF.

Scott, Foresman and Company

CHICAGO   ATLANTA   DALLAS   NEW YORK

Stories

IN THE CITY NEIGHBORHOOD

IN THE COUNTRY NEIGHBORHOOD

David
at the
Country School

David's School

This is David's school,
a one room school in the country.

Big children, little children,
brothers and sisters
are all in one room.

And they are all David's friends.

It is night, and the children
are home in bed now.

But they will all come back
to the one room country school.

Big children, little children,
brothers and sisters.

David's friends and David, too.

Hello, David

Away went David to school.

"Go fast, Tim," he said.

"I want to get to school soon."

Trot, trot went the little pony
with David.

Trot, trot, trot, trot.

Down the road to school.

Honk, honk, honk!

Down the road came Jack.

"Hello, David!" he called.

"Good-by! Good-by!"

And he laughed and laughed.

"Oh, Tim," David said.

"See Jack in the car.

Now he will get to school first."

Trot, trot, trot!

David and the little pony
went on down the road.

Soon they came to the car
with Jack in it.

David laughed and laughed.
"This is fun," he thought.
"That old car will not go.
Now I will get to school first."

"Hello, Jack," he called.
"Good-by! Good-by!"

David and the little pony went on.

But David was not happy.

Soon he said, "Stop, Tim, stop.

You and I must help Jack

so he can get to school on time."

Back went David and Tim
to the old car.

And away went the little pony
with the two boys.

They did get to school on time.

Work at the Country School

Here is Miss Black helping
David and Jack read.

How is the big girl helping
Miss Black?

Dick wants to make something
that will fly.

But first he must read how
to make it.

Tell what he wants to make.

A Rabbit Comes to Lunch

The children in David's school
did not go home for lunch.

They ate at the school, and
so did Miss Black.

"I hear a dog," Miss Black said
at lunch time.

"What is he doing?

Children, do you hear a dog?"

"I hear a dog," said David.
And all the children said, "Yes!
We hear one, too."
"Bow-wow," said the dog.
"Bow-wow-wow-wow! Bow-wow!"

Miss Black went to look.
"Oh, children!" she said.
"Come and see.
A big dog is running
after a rabbit."

The children ran to the door.

"Come on, little rabbit, come on!"
called David and Jack.

On came the rabbit, but
on came the big dog, too.

"Oh, Miss Black!" said Sally.

"Can't we do something to help
the little rabbit?

Can't we do something?"

Miss Black thought fast.

"Get back, children," she called,
"into the school house! Now!"

In ran the children.
Jump! In went the rabbit.
And in ran Miss Black after him.
But the big dog did not get in.
Bang went the door.
"Bow-wow-wow," said the big dog.
"Bow-wow-wow-wow-wow!"

The New Pet

"Pretty little rabbit," said Sally.

"The big dog can not get you now.

Come to me, little rabbit."

But the rabbit did not come.

Miss Black said, "The little rabbit
will not come to you now, Sally.

But maybe he will come to you
after we eat lunch.

Let's eat our lunch now."

The children ate lunch.

Hop, hop went the little rabbit
here and there, here and there.

After lunch Dick said, "Come to me,
little rabbit.

I will make a house for you,
and you can be our school pet."

But the rabbit did not come.

Hop, hop, hop he went
here and there, here and there.

Then David said, "See what I
have for you, little rabbit.

It was in my school lunch.

But I did not eat it.

I wanted you to have it.

Come and get it, little rabbit."

Hop, hop went the rabbit to David.

"Oh, what a funny carrot man," laughed Sally.

"Look, look," said David.

"Little rabbit likes my carrot man. So let's name him Mr. Carrot."

"Yes! Mr. Carrot is a good name for our pet," the children said.

"And a carrot is a good lunch for him," said Miss Black.

"Hello, Mr. Carrot, hello!"

A House for Mr. Carrot

Dick was a big boy.

He could make good rabbit houses.

Bang! Bang! Dick was making

a house for Mr. Carrot.

How did David and Jack help?

Helping Miss Black

David and Jack thought it was fun
to help Miss Black after school.

Look at this picture and tell
how they are helping her.

At the one room country school there was work to do every day.

But the children were good helpers.

So Miss Black did not have to do all the work.

Look at the picture.

Tell how Dick is helping her.

Tell how the girl is helping.

How do you help at your school?

Ding-dong Bell

Ding-dong went the school bell.

Ding-dong, ding-dong, ding-dong.

And into the school house went
all the children.

Four times a day the bell went
ding-dong, ding-dong, ding-dong.

And the children came running.

"I wish I could ring the bell,"
thought David.

"I wish I could ring the bell,"
thought Jack.

Miss Black let the big children
ring the bell.

But she did not let Jack and David
ring it at all.

One day David said to Jack,
"The big children ring the bell
all the time.

I wish you and I were big."

"So do I," said Jack.

Dick was a big boy.

He helped Miss Black every day.

But one day he was not at school.

"Jack," said David, "you and I
are not big like Dick.

But the two of us can do
what one big boy can do."

So they did the work that Dick
did when he was at school.

"Thank you," Miss Black said.

"You boys are good helpers.

Good helpers like you may ring the bell for me."

"May we, Miss Black?" said Jack.

"Oh, may we?" said David.

And they ran to get the bell.

Soon it was time for the children to go in to school.

Ding-dong, ding-dong went the bell.

And it was Jack and David who made it ring.

The Party

One night after dark the children all came back to the country school.

And the little sisters and brothers came, too.

So did the mothers and fathers.

And so did the grandmothers and grandfathers.

They all came to a party.

The mothers and grandmothers
came with food for the party.
Oh, what good food it was!

Soon it was time to eat.
"I like this party," said Ruth.
Ruth was David's little sister.
"This is a good, good party."

After dinner they all had fun.

"Look, Dick," laughed David.

"Look at your father."

"Oh, Father," said Dick.

"You are too big for our school."

"No, Dick," said his father.

"The things in your school are
too little for me."

He laughed and laughed.

At last it was time to go home.
"Good-by, Miss Black," David called.
"Good-by, Dick. Good-by, Jack."
Oh, how sleepy David was,
and how sleepy Ruth was, too.

The day after the party David
did not have to get up for school.
It was not a school day.
Guess what day it was.

The Mothers and Fathers Help

Here are some of the mothers and fathers helping at David's school.

How are the fathers helping?

How are the mothers helping?

Hello and Good-by

One morning all David's friends were at school.

But David was not there.

"Where is David?" said Miss Black.

"Jack, did you see him this morning on the road to school?"

"No, Miss Black," Jack said.

"I did not see him at all."

"David is always on time," said Dick.

"Where is David?"

"Here I am," said David.
"I came to say hello and good-by."

Sally said, "Oh, David, how funny.
We do not say hello and good-by
when we come to school.
We just say hello."

"I must say hello and good-by
this morning," David said.
"My father and mother have
a new farm.
So I can not go to this school.
I must go to another one."

"We wish you did not have to go,"
said Miss Black.

"Where is your new farm?"

David said, "Our new farm
is just a little way from the city.

So I must go to the city school.

Look! Father made this picture
so you could see where I must go.

See our old farm and this school.

See our new farm and the city."

The children looked and looked.

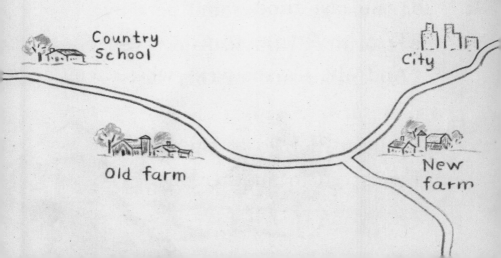

Country
School

City

Old farm

New
farm

"I do not want to go away
from this school," David said.

"All my friends are here."

"Take Mr. Carrot," said Jack.

"Then you will always have
one friend from this school."

"Yes," said all the children.

"Take Mr. Carrot with you."

"Oh, thank you," said David.

So home went David and Tim
from the country school
for the last time.

Trot, trot, trot, trot.

And Mr. Carrot went with them.

David
at the
City School

The New Farm

Honk! Honk! Honk!
This is the road to the city.
David's new farm is on this road.
So David will ride to school
in this big yellow school bus.

Honk! Honk! Honk!
Every day David will ride
to the big city school.
He can not go to the country school.
He must go to the city school now.
The big, big school in the city.

Hello, David

It was time for David to go
to the city school.

Honk! Honk! Honk!

Along came the big bus, and
it stopped for David.

"Hello, David," called the man
in the bus.

"Your father said you were going
to the city school this morning.

We are going there, too."

"Hello, David, hello,"
called the children in the bus.

"We know your name."

"Oh, Mother," said David.

"The children all know me."

"Yes, David," said his mother.

"And you will soon know them.

It will be fun to ride
in that big bus every day.

And it will be fun to go
to a big city school
Good-by, David, good-by."

Away went the bus with David
and the other children.

"I wish I could go to school,"
Ruth said to her mother.

"Ee-ee-ee-ee," went Tim, and he
began to run after David.

"Look, Mother," said Ruth. "Tim
wants to go to school, too."

"Ee-ee-ee," went Tim again.

But David did not hear.

He was on his way to the city school.

Come Along with Me

"Well!" said David when they
came to the school.

"I thought city schools were big.
But not this big.
How can I find my room?"

"Just come along with me,"
said another boy from the bus.

"I will take you to the principal."

Mr. Town was the principal.

David had a letter for him
from Miss Black.

"Well, well," said the principal
as soon as he began to read it.

"So you went to a one room school
in the country.

When I was a boy, I went
to a country school, too."

"Oh, Mr. Town," David said.

"Did you live on a farm?"

"Yes, David," said the principal.

"And our school had just one room.

It was a good school.

But city schools are good, too.

You will like this one.

Just come along with me, and I

will take you to your room."

David and the principal walked
along. They saw first one door
and then another.

But at last Mr. Town stopped
and said, "Here is your room."

Then they went in.

There was Miss Bell.

And what a surprise! There was
David's old friend, Tom White.

"Oh, Miss Bell," Tom said.

"David did live on the farm
next to my grandfather's farm.

He is one of my good friends."

"Well, David," said Miss Bell.

"I am glad you have one friend
at this school.

Now you will not get lost."

"Oh, Miss Bell," laughed David.

"I know I could not get lost
at this school.

I am glad to see Tom again.

But I could not get lost here.

When I do not know where to go,
some one always says,

'Just come along with me.'
And that is what I do."

David Sees the School

Many, many children can go
to this room at one time.

Tom said, "This is where we
come when we have an assembly.
We come here to play, too."

What is an assembly?

This is the lunch room.

Some children eat lunch here
every day.

Some children eat lunch here
when it rains or snows.

Do you eat lunch at school
every school day?

Do you eat lunch at school
just when it rains or snows?

Miss Street helps all the children,
and she helped David.

What is Miss Street?

Tom took David to see Mr. Brown.

What is Mr. Brown?

In David's Room

The children in David's room sang
and sang. David sang, too.

Then the children began to read
some pretty blue books.

David had a book to read, too.

"I like this book," he thought.

Then some of the children
made pictures.

So David made a picture
of the one room country school.

"See what I made," David said
to Jim, one of the other boys.

Jim looked at David's picture.

"Oh, what a funny picture," he said

And he laughed and laughed.

"It is not a funny picture,"
David said.

But he put it in his pocket.

He put it in his pocket
so the other children could not see it.

That night David's family wanted to see what he had made at school.

So he let them see the picture he had in his pocket.

Mr. Hill said, "I like this."

Mrs. Hill said, "Let's put it up where we can see it all the time."

And Ruth said, "David can make pretty pictures, can't he?"

Then David was happy again.

When he made another picture, he let all the children see it.

No one laughed but Jim.

"Well!" thought David, "Jim is just one boy.

The other children like my picture. And so do I!"

David's Turn

"Look, David," said Tom one day
when they went out to play.

"Jip is here at school.

Funny Jip! He likes to slide
down the slide with us."

Down the slide came Jip and Susan White.

And down came Jane after them.

"Hello," called Susan when she saw David with her brother, Tom.

"Come and slide down the slide. You may have my turn."

"Thanks," said David.

But just then Jim came running up and pushed David away from the slide.

"Jim!" said Tom. "It is not your turn. Let David slide first."

"No, I want to go first," said Jim. And up the slide he went.

"I wish Jim did not go to this school," David thought.

"I don't like that boy."

Jim sat down on the slide.

"Bow-wow," said Jip.

He wanted another ride.

So up the slide he went and
jumped up on Jim.

"Stop, stop," called Jim.

"Help! Help!

Tom, make your dog stop."

Down the slide went Jim,
head first, with Jip on him.

"I fell!" Jim said.

"I fell down the slide!

That dog jumped on me.   So I fell."

"Don't be a baby," laughed Jane.

"Jip was just playing."

And David said, "You wanted

to go down the slide first, Jim.

And you did go down first.

Head first!"

Thank You, Mr. Brown

One day Sally said, "I have
a new puppy, and I am going
to paint a picture of him."

She began to paint a picture
of a puppy with a funny little tail.

The other children began to paint
pictures of toys and pets, too.

Then Miss Bell put the pictures up
where all the children could see them.

David painted a picture of his pony.

He painted Mr. Carrot, and his hen,
his dog Spot, and his cat Mew-mew.

"See all of David's pets," said Tom.

"One, two, three, four, five.
David has five pets."

"He has a pony," said Jim.

"I wish I had a pony."

"He has a rabbit," said Jane.

"I wish we had a rabbit here
at school."

"Do you?" said David.

"Then you may have Mr. Carrot."

But Jim said, "First we must make
a rabbit house for him to live in.

I know how to make one."

"We will help," said the others.

The children worked and worked.
But David did not like the house
that they made.

"We must make a good house,"
he said, "or Mr. Carrot will run away."

"Maybe Mr. Brown will help us,"
said Billy.

"I know that he could make
a good rabbit house."

Mr. Brown was a busy man, but he
was glad to help the children.

The next day Mr. Carrot came
to the city school with David.

He saw the fine new house, and he
saw a big yellow carrot in it.

Hop went Mr. Carrot into the house.

The children were so happy that
they just looked and looked.

"Now we have a school pet,"
they said.

"Thank you, David.
Thank you, Mr. Brown."

Mr. Brown Again

Mr. Brown can do many things.
Do you have a good helper
like Mr. Brown at your school?
What is his name?

Peter Comes to School

Splash! Splash! Splash!

Down came the rain.

David saw Mrs. White and Peter come to school with Tom and Susan.

"Hello," said David. "Did you come to hear Tom and me read?"

"No, David," said Mrs. White.

"I came to see the principal.

Susan has lost her umbrella, and I must find it or get her a new one."

When they saw Mr. Town, he said,
"What color is your umbrella?"

"Red," said Susan. "There it is
under that big ball.

Oh, I am so glad I have found it."

"Ball, ball," called Peter.

And Mr. Town said, "Peter, I wish
you could have that ball.

But some little boy lost it, and
soon he will come here to find it."

"Ball, ball," said Peter again.

Susan said, "That green ball is
the color of one he has at home.
So he thinks that ball is his."

"Come, Peter," said Mrs. White.
"Susan has found her umbrella.
Now you and I must go home."

But Peter did not want to go home.
He wanted the big green ball.

"Oh, Mother," said Susan. "Peter
is too little to come to school."

David said, "I know what I can do
to make Peter happy."

Away he ran, and soon he came back
with something funny for Peter.

"Look, Peter," he said. "I made
this funny cow in school.

You may have it.

Moo, Peter. Moo, moo."

Peter looked and looked.
Then he began to laugh.
"Moo, moo," said Peter.

Hurry! Hurry! Hurry!

One day after lunch the children
were all coming back to school.

Tom saw his friend, Mrs. Gray.

And he stopped to talk.

Then the school bell began to ring.

As soon as the bell began to ring,
the children began to run.

"That boy is running over my yard,"
Mrs. Gray said to Tom.

"How can I have a pretty yard
when so many children run over it?

I wish I did not live next door
to a school."

"Oh, Mrs. Gray," Tom said.

"I always run over your yard,
too, when I am in a hurry.

I guess I don't stop to think
what my feet will do to it."

"Well, Tom," laughed Mrs. Gray.

"I guess that is why the others run over my yard.

They just don't stop to think.

I like children, but I like a pretty green yard, too.

So please ask all your friends to stop and think after this."

"Yes, Mrs. Gray," Tom said.

Then he began to laugh, too.

"But, Mrs. Gray," he said.

"The children can't stop and think after they hear the last bell ring.

I guess they will have to run and think.

They will have to run and think where they are running."

A Good Assembly

The children in the city school
were all coming to an assembly.

Big children, little children,
brothers and sisters.

David's new friends and David, too.

David thought, "Now this school is like the country school.

All the children are in one room."

Then he saw Tom.
Tom was with the principal.
"Why is Tom up there?" he thought.
But he could not guess.
All the other children thought,
"Why is Tom with the principal?"
But they could not guess.
Just then Mr. Town began to talk.
"Boys and girls," he said.
"Mrs. Gray lives next to our school.
So she is our neighbor, and we are her neighbors.
But we are not very good neighbors.
Tom White will tell you why."

What a surprise! Tom White
was going to talk at the assembly.

He said, "This is what Mrs. Gray
asked me to tell you.

She works and works to have
a pretty yard, but we walk on it.

There are so many of us that
our feet make it brown.

Please do not walk or run
over her yard again."

Up jumped Billy Snow.

"Good for Tom," said Billy Snow.

"We don't have to walk over yards.

We can walk on the walks.

That is why they are called walks."

"Yes," thought the children.

"That is why they are called walks."

Then Billy asked, "May Tom tell
our neighbor that we will not walk
over her yard again?"

And every one of the children
in that assembly said, "Yes."

"That was a good assembly," the children said.

After that day the children always walked on the walks.

Soon a letter came to the principal.

It was for all the children.

Mr. Town called another assembly so the children could hear the letter.

This is what it said.

ar Neighbors:
You do walk on the walks now. You are making me very happy.

Happy to have a pretty yard. And happy to have good neighbors.

Your friend,
Mrs. Gray

In the City Neighborhood

The City Neighborhood

Houses and houses and houses.
Houses and stores and
a big school.
This is a city neighborhood.

All day the neighborhood
is a busy neighborhood.

The children of the neighborhood
are busy, too.

But they are in school.

Yes or No

"Let's take a trip," said Tom.

"Let's take a trip to the park."

"Yes, let's," said the children.

They all wanted to take a trip to the park.

Miss Bell said they could go.

Mr. Town, the principal, said they could go.

And that night the mothers and fathers all said they could go.

But the next day, just as they were going out of the school room, David called to them.

"Stop, stop," he called.

"We can not go to the park now."

"Why can't we go to the park?"
the children asked. "Why?"

"Look at the rabbit house, and
you will see," David said.

The door of the rabbit house was
open. Mr. Carrot was not there.

"Oh, oh! The door is open, and
Mr. Carrot has run away," Jane said.

Then the children began to look
everywhere for the little rabbit.

They looked behind doors, and
they looked under things.

But they could not find him.

They went to the assembly room
and began looking there.

He was not in the assembly room.

"We have looked everywhere,"
Jim said. "Let's go to the park."

"No, no," said Jane.

"We must look for Mr. Carrot."

"Maybe he went outdoors,"
David said.

"Maybe he went down the street.

Oh, Miss Bell, may we go outdoors
and look for him?"

"Ask the other children what they
want to do," Miss Bell said.

So David asked, "How many of you
want to go to the park now?"

"I do," said Patty.

"I do," said Jim.

"How many of you want to look
for the rabbit?" David asked.

"We do," said all the others.

So Patty and Jim did what
the others wanted to do.

They went to look for Mr. Carrot.

Where Is Mr. Carrot?

Down the street went the children
looking for the little bunny.

They did not see him, but they
saw a neighbor at work in her yard.

"Did you see a bunny?" they asked.

"Yes," she said. "He was eating
something in my yard.

But when I came outdoors,
he stopped eating and ran away."

So the children walked on.

"Look," said Jim. "We are coming
to my house. See my baby sister.
She just sleeps and sleeps."
Billy said, "We are coming
to my house, too. See my new puppy."
"I live next to Billy," said Jill.
"See my cat and her kittens."
"We see them," said the children.
"We see them all!"
But they did not see Mr. Carrot.
So they walked on.

"This is where my brother works,"
Sally Field said. "Here he is.

Did you see our bunny?" she asked.

"Yes," said her brother.

"He ran down that next street.

But I was very busy just then.

So there was nothing I could do
to stop him."

"Dear me," said Jane.

"We must hurry."

And they all walked faster.

They saw Dick's house and the man
who came to Dick's house with milk.

They saw Jane's house and the man
who came to Jane's house with letters.

Then they saw Mr. Carrot
in the grocery store eating carrots.

And the grocery man saw him, too.

Out came Mr. Carrot in a hurry.
"Oh, Mr. Carrot!!!" said David.

The grocery man began to laugh.
"So he is Mr. Carrot," he said.
"Well, that is a surprise.
I have always had carrots
in my grocery store.
But this is the first time
I have had a Mr. Carrot."

Back at School Again

"There, Mr. Carrot," said David.

"You can't push the door open now.

You can't run away when we want
to take a trip to the park."

"Well," said Billy. "We did have
a trip to the grocery. That was fun."

"Yes," said the other children.

"Let's make a story of our trip
and make pictures of it, too."

So that is what they did.

And that is what you will see next.

Mr. Carrot and the Grocery Man

Here is Mr. Carrot
looking for carrots.

Here we are
looking for Mr. Carrot.

This is the grocery
store where he
found the carrots.
And it is the
grocery store
where we found him.

A Trip to the Park

One day the children did take
a trip to the park.

But the park was not
in the school neighborhood.

So they went on the street car.

Soon David said, "What big stores!
We must be down town now."

"Yes," said Jim.

"My grandmother and grandfather
work in that store over there."

"There is the store where my father
works," Billy said.

And Tom said, "My father works
away up there."

"Well, well," said Miss Bell.

"Your fathers are neighbors
at home and neighbors at work."

When the street car came to the park, David jumped up.

But the car stopped with a bump. And down went David.

"David!" said Nancy. "Don't get up when the street car is going. It always stops with a bump."

"I just found that out," said David.

Jim Feeds the Squirrels

First the children went to see
the animals.

"Oh, Jim," laughed Miss Bell.

"What have you in your pockets?
You must not feed the animals."

"I can feed squirrels," Jim said.

"I have some nuts for them.
Let's find some squirrels."

So they all walked on.

Soon a little brown squirrel
with a big tail came running up.

"Here, little squirrel," said Jim.

Away ran the little squirrel, and
he took the nut with him.

Soon another and another squirrel
came running to Jim.

"They know you have some nuts
for them," Miss Bell said.

Sally Field said, "Please give us some nuts, Jim.

We want to feed the squirrels, too."

"No," said Jim. "I want to feed them, and I am going to do it."

"Miss Bell, please make Jim give us some nuts," Ellen said.

But Miss Bell said, "No, Ellen.

You must not ask me to do that.

I do not want to make Jim give you the nuts.

But I wish he thought of others now and then."

"Well," said David, "he did think of the squirrels.

I am glad of that.

It is fun to see them eat!"

Fast As the Wind

Sally Field and David had
toy boats to play with.

Sally's boat was painted blue.

David's boat was painted red.

Along came a puff of wind.

Faster and faster went the boats.

"Look!" said Sally. "The wind
is making our boats go fast."

The children ran to get the boats.

"My boat is coming in first,"
Sally Field called.

David's red boat was coming along
just behind Sally's blue boat.

"Next time my boat will be first,"
David said.

And next time his boat was first.

Sally and David let some
of the other children play, too.

"Let me have your boat now,"
Jim said to David.

"No," said David. "I don't want
you to have it."

Jim ran to Miss Bell.
"Please make David give me
his boat," he said.

But Miss Bell just asked,
"Did I make you give any nuts
to the other children?"

"No," Jim said. "But next time
I will give them some."

Miss Bell said, "I am glad, Jim."
But the children did not hear him.
They were too busy playing.

David let Nancy have his boat.

Puff, puff went the wind, and away went the boat.

Then the wind stopped, and the boat stopped, too.

"Look, David," Nancy called.
"See what your boat is doing.
Hurry! Hurry!
We must hurry and get it."
But no one could get it.

"Bow-wow," said Jip, and in
he went after the boat.

"Oh, oh," laughed the children.

"Jip knows what to do.

Good old Jip!"

"Look, Nancy," laughed David.

"See how fast the boat is going.

Jip can make the boat go as fast
as the wind."

The Merry-go-round

Soon the children saw
a merry-go-round in the park.

"Merry-go-round, merry-go-round!"
called the children.

And they all jumped on.

But they did not go round.

Then David saw something that
he could push.

"Look," he said. "I am making
the merry-go-round go.

But not very fast."

"Now I see what to do," Tom said.

"See me push! And I can push
with my feet, too."

"So can we," called the others.

And they all began to push.

They pushed and pushed!

Round and round went
the merry-go-round.

Faster and faster and faster.

"This is fun," said Patty.

"I could do this all day."

"Look, Miss Bell," Tom called.

"See us go round. We are all making the merry-go-round go."

"I see," laughed Miss Bell.

"But you must stop now.

It is time to go home."

"I know how we can stop," Jim said.

"David, you must stop first.

Tom, you stop next.

Then Billy can stop.

Then Patty and Jill and the others."

So David stopped.

Tom stopped.

The merry-go-round went slower and slower and slower.

When all the children had stopped,
the merry-go-round stopped, too.

The children jumped down and ran
to Miss Bell.

"We all helped make it go, and we
all helped make it stop," Jim said.

"It was fun."

"Yes, Jim," said Miss Bell.

"Children always have fun
when they play that way."

City Neighborhoods

A city has many neighborhoods.

The children saw this neighborhood
on the way home.

Do you have a neighborhood
like this in your town?

Where is it?

Miss Bell Talks to Jim

One day David came to school
with a letter from his mother.

It was a letter for Miss Bell and
the children in David's room.

Mrs. Hill wanted them to come
and have dinner at the farm.

"Thank you, David," Miss Bell said.

"And the children will thank you,
too, when I read them this letter.

They will be glad to come to dinner.

And I know they will want to see
how you live and work on a farm."

"Well," David said.

"I like trips in the city.

So I think city children will like a trip to a farm."

Then he said, "But I don't want Jim to come.

He will not take turns, and the other children don't like him.

Please do not ask Jim."

Miss Bell looked at David.

"Jim is in our room, David," she said. "What the children in our room do, he must do, too.

Do you want our room to come to your farm?

Or don't you?"

"Yes, I do," David said.

Then Miss Bell said to David,
"I think Jim wants the children
to like him.

I do not think he is very happy.
I will talk to him.
You will see. We will all have
a good time at your farm.
And so will Jim."

Miss Bell did talk to Jim.
What do you think she said
to him?

In the Country Neighborhood

Morning at David's Farm

Moo-oo-oo! Here come the cows
up from the pasture.

Cluck, cluck, cluck, quack, quack
go the hens and the ducks.

It is time for David to jump
out of bed.

Morning is a busy time on a farm.

David's father must milk the cows
and feed all the animals.

And David will help him.

Good Farm Helpers

Bill works for the Hills.

How is Bill helping?

How is David helping?

Here They Come

It was time for David's friends
to come to the farm.

David and his father were helping
Mother get a good dinner.

But Ruth was down at the road,
looking and looking and looking.

"Here they come, David,"
she called. "Here they come!"

David ran to see.

"Oh, Ruth," he said. "That is our neighbor, Mr. Green.

Maybe he took some hens and roosters to town this morning.

Now he is coming home again.

Look! He is not in a bus.

My friends will come in a bus."

David went back to the house.

But soon Ruth called again,

"Here they come! Here they come!"

David ran to see.

Along came a big bus, and on down the road it went.

"That was a bus," said Ruth.

"Yes," said David, "but not the bus from our school.

Oh, Ruth! I can't run out here every time a bus comes along.

I am busy helping Mother.

Why don't you go to the orchard and play with your pets and toys?"

So Ruth went to the orchard.

Honk! Honk! Down the road
came the school bus at last.

"Mother! Father! Ruth!"
David called. "Here they come!"

There were Miss Bell and
the children from David's room.
And there were Susan and Jip.
They had come, too.

"Look at Jip's tail go," Tom said.
"He sees his friend, Spot."

"Yes," said Susan. "Now we are
all here but Ruth. Where is she?"
"Dear me," said Mrs. Hill. "She
was looking for you all morning.
But now we must look for her."
"I know where she is," David said.
"She is playing in the orchard."
So they all went to the orchard.

There was Ruth in the orchard.

There was Mrs. Quack, the duck,
and Mew-mew with her three kittens.

"Oh, oh," laughed Susan. "We
have found Ruth and her pets, too."

Just then Ruth sat up.

"David! David!" she said.

"Here they are!"

"Yes, Ruth," laughed Miss Bell.

"Here we are, and what a good time
we are all going to have!"

Jip's Turn

The children wanted to ride Tim.

So they all went to the pasture.

"Me first, me first! Let me
ride first!" they all called.

And this time it was Jim
who said, "We must take turns."

"Yes," said David.

"You must all take turns.

Let the girls ride first."

So May had the first turn.

Tim walked up and down the pasture
with May.

He walked up and down the pasture
with all the girls.

But when the boys began to ride,
they thought he was too poky.

"Get up, Tim, get up," they said.

"Don't be so poky."

And away went Tim,
galloping, galloping, galloping.

Soon it was dinner time, and
Miss Bell came to get the children.
She met Jim galloping along.
"Look, Miss Bell," he called.
"See how well I can ride.
And I took the last turn, too."
"Fine, Jim!" said Miss Bell.
Jim jumped down from the pony.
"Bow-wow!" said Jip.
"Now it is Jip's turn," Tom said.
"Jip likes to ride a pony."

"Yes," said Susan. "Our grandfather
has a pony, too.

Jip always rides Grandfather's pony
when we go to Grandfather's farm."

Away went Tim with Jip.

Oh, what fun it was
to see a dog ride a pony!

"Well, Jim," laughed Miss Bell.
"You did not have to take
the last turn after all.

Jip's turn is the last turn."

Dinner in the Orchard

The children all ate dinner in
the orchard under the apple trees.

"M-m-m!" Sally Field said.

"You have good things to eat
on your farm, David!"

Just then something went
peep, peep, peep.

"Look up in the apple tree
over Dick's head," Billy said.

"The robins have a nest
in this orchard.

I see four baby robins."

"I see them!" Jill said.

"Funny baby robins!
They want dinner, too."

"Here comes Mother Robin now
with some dinner," said Miss Bell.

"Father Robin is just behind her.
The baby birds are too little
to fly away from the nest.

So the big birds must fly away
and get dinner for them."

"That is a funny dinner," said Jill.

"But I guess the baby birds like it."

Jill was so busy looking up
at the nest that she stopped
eating her cookie.

All at once Father Robin
came down from the apple tree.
Swish! Swish!
Away he went with the cookie.
"Oh! Oh!" laughed David.
"Father Robin is like Jill.
He is not like the baby birds.
He wants a cookie for dinner."

Making Money

Ellen said, "I wish our family had an apple orchard."

"Oh, Ellen," said David, "there is no room for orchards in a city.

That is why we take apples from the farm to the city.

We take many other things, too.

Then we get money for them, and you get food to eat."

Jill asked, "Do the eggs we buy at the grocery come from your farm?"

"Maybe," said David.

Mrs. Hill said, "Come with me, and you will see eggs, hens, roosters, and wee little yellow chickens, too."

Peep, peep, peep, peep!

There were wee yellow chickens
everywhere.

"What a pretty color they are,"
Jill said.

"Where did you get so many?"

"I know," said Billy. "Hens sat
on eggs for days and days and days.

Then little chickens came out
of the eggs."

"Hens sat on some of the eggs," Mrs. Hill said. "But we put some eggs in this machine, too.

Soon wee chickens will come out of the eggs in the machine."

"Look, look!" said Jill. "I see five little yellow chickens now.

Oh, Mrs. Hill! This machine is just like a mother hen."

"It is a funny looking hen," laughed Billy.

Helping on the Farm

The children wanted to help David find eggs, and they did help.

"Look," said Jim at last.

"There is nothing at all in the nests. The eggs are all in our baskets."

"Fine," said Mrs. Hill.

"But Mr. Hill can not take eggs to town in baskets.

So come with me, and you will see where to put them."

The children worked and worked.

"Look," said Jim. "Now there is nothing at all in the baskets."

"Fine," said Mrs. Hill.

"You children are good helpers."

"Oh, my," thought David. "I am glad I asked Jim to come to the farm.

He likes to help.

And he takes turns.

The other children like him now.

And I like him, too."

The Birthday Hen

"This is my birthday hen,"
David said. "I asked Mother
to give her to me for my birthday.

Father takes her eggs to town
with the other eggs, and I get
pennies for them."

"How many pennies do you have?"
Tom asked.

"Not any pennies now," said David.

"I took them all to the store
to buy a birthday doll for Ruth."

"Here is my doll," Ruth said.
"I have a doll bed for her, too.

See how sleepy she is.

She can sleep and say ma-ma, too."

Ma-ma, ma-ma went the doll.

"Well, well," said Miss Bell.

"So the birthday hen made money
to buy a birthday doll.

It must be fun to live on a farm
and have pets like that."

"It is fun," David said.

"But it is work, too."

A Ride with the Horses

When the children came out
of the hen house, they met Mr. Hill.
He was on a big farm wagon.
"Jump up on the wagon," he said.
"We will go for a ride."
Soon Miss Bell and the children
were all on the wagon.
Bump, bump, bump.
Away they all went.

First they came to the corn field.

"See our corn," Mr. Hill said.

"It is just coming up."

"What do you do with corn?"
asked Jane.

"We eat it," said Mr. Hill.

"And so do the horses and the cows,
the pigs and the hens, the roosters
and the ducks.

Corn is a good food."

The wagon bumped along and bumped along behind the horses.

The children saw one field after another.

They saw the cow pasture and other pastures, too.

"I like this ride," Jill said.

"The horses are poky, but I am glad they do not go any faster.

There are so many things to see. And I want to see them all."

Animal Houses

Farm animals are not always in the pasture.

They have houses where they can go when it rains or snows.

Which animal houses do you see?

A Funny Name

As the wagon bumped along home,
the children met Spot, Jip, and Bill.

"Look," laughed David.

"Spot is doing his farm work, and
now he has a good helper.

Jip went to the pasture to help
Spot get the cows."

"Do the cows have names?"
asked Ellen.

"Some of them do," said David.
"Valentine has a name."

"Valentine!" said the children.

"What a funny name for a cow.
Which one is Valentine?"

"Guess," said David.

The children looked at the cows.
Sally said, "Valentines are red.

But all your cows are red, and
just one is called Valentine."

Then Billy said, "I don't know
which cow is Valentine.

But I think that I know
why you called her that.

She came on Valentine Day."

"No, no! You can not guess why
her name is Valentine," said David.
"But you will soon see."

Then he jumped out of the wagon
and ran to one of the cows.

"Turn your head," he said.

And he pushed her head round
so the children could see it.

"Oh, oh," laughed the children.

"Valentine is a good name
for that cow!"

Jim Milks a Cow

"Are you going to milk the cows?"
Jim asked Mr. Hill.

"Yes, Jim," said Mr. Hill.

And then he said, "We always
milk in the barn.

But I will milk one cow out here.

Then you can see how I do it."

Mr. Hill sat down and began to milk.

Swish! Swish! Swish!

Down came the milk.

"Now I see how to do it," said Jim.

So he sat down.

He worked and worked.

But no milk came.

"Why can't I get any milk

out of the cow?" he asked.

"Look, Jim," said David.

"This is the way to milk."

Swish! Swish! Swish!
Down came the milk.
"Look, David can milk,"
all the children said at once.

"Now I do see how to milk,"
said Jim.
And he sat down again.
Swish went the milk just once.
"Hear that," said Mr. Hill.
"Jim did milk a little."

"Some day I will have a farm,"
Jim said.

"Then I will milk all the cows.
It is fun to milk."

"It is not fun to milk when you
have as many cows as I have,"
said Mr. Hill.

"It is not fun to milk cows
day after day after day.

When you have a farm, you will be
glad to let a machine milk."

"A machine!" said the children.
"Can a machine milk?"

"A machine can milk," said Mr. Hill.
"And it can milk two cows at once.
Come into the barn and see
how well a machine can milk."

The children looked and looked.

"It is a good machine," said Jim.

"But I think it is fun to milk the other way.

When I have a farm, that is how I am going to milk."

Other Farm Machines

This is one of David's neighbors.

What is the man doing?

Do you see a pasture, a field,

or an orchard in the picture?

This woman has a machine.
What is the machine called?
What is the woman doing with it?

This woman has a machine, too.
Can we buy what she is making
at a grocery store?

The Farm and the City

"Pig, pig, pig," called Bill.

"Hear that," said Miss Bell
to David's friends.

"It is time for Bill to feed the pigs.
We must go home now.

It will get dark, and you must not
be away from home after dark."

Soon they all said good-by, and
away they went in the big bus.

One day soon after that
a letter came to the Hill family.

It was a thank you letter
from David's friends at school.

And some pictures came with it.

David said, "See the funny story.

See the funny pictures, Ruth."

Then he began to read the story
of the big fat pig.

The Big Fat Pig

This is
the big fat pig
at the farm.

This is
the big fat pig
at the store.

"See this picture," said Mr. Hill.
"See the orchard and the field.
See the pastures and the barn.
It looks just like our farm.
Look! There is our cat, Mew-mew,
with her three kittens."

What animals are in the pastures?

What is in the field?

What is in the orchard?

What color is the house?

Is David's house that color?

Now go on with the story.

"Look, Father," said David. "See
Sally's father at work in the city.
See Dick's father and Jane's father
and all the other fathers, too."

"I see," said Mr. Hill.

"Well, David, there are many ways
to work and make money in a city.

Maybe you will want to work
in the city when you are big."

"No, Father," said David. "It is
fun to go to school in the city.

But I am going to live on a farm
and work on a farm always.

Just like you!"

To the Teacher

Hello, David is the third social-development book in the *Social Studies Program* of the Curriculum Foundation Series. The understandings and behavior traits emphasized in each unit are listed on pages 157-160.

All the words in *Hello, David* except the 180 listed below are used in the preceding books of this program, *Tom and Susan* and *Peter's Family*. For children who have completed *Our New Friends*, the first reader of *The New Basic Reading Program* of the Curriculum Foundation Series, only the 30 words printed in boldface type in the list below will be new.

Vocabulary List

UNIT I

5	**David**	17	him	30 had
	country		bang	his
6	—	18	maybe	things
7	night		let's	31 last
	back	19	then	sleepy
8	Tim	20	**carrot**	32 some
	trot		Mr.	33 morning
	road	21	could	**always**
9	**honk**		**making**	34 just
	called	22	her	another
	first	23	every	35 way
10	thought		day	**city**
	old		were	36 take
11	stop	24	**ding-dong**	them
	time		**bell**	
12	**Miss**	25	wish	**UNIT II**
	read		**ring**	
13	fly		let	37 —
14	**lunch**	26	us	38 **bus**
	hear		when	39 —
15	running	27	may	40 along
	after		made	stopped
16	door	28	party	41 know
	Sally		dark	be
	can't	29	food	42 other
			Ruth	began

	again
43	**principal**
44	Town
	as
45	live
46	walked
	surprise
47	next
	glad
	lost
48	many
	an
	assembly
49	rains
	or
	snows
50	Street
	took
	Brown
51	sang
	books
52	Jim
	put
	pocket
53	Hill
	Mrs.

154

54 **turn**
   slide
55 pushed
   don't
56 head
57 fell
58 puppy
   paint
59 Spot
   five
   has
60 Billy
61 busy
   fine
62 —
63 splash
   umbrella
64 color
   found
65 green
   thinks
66 moo
67 hurry
   coming
   Gray
68 over
   feet
69 why
   ask
70 —
71 **neighbor**
   very
72 —
73 —

74 dear

UNIT III

75 **neighborhood**
76 —
77 —
78 **trip**
   park
79 open
80 behind
81 Patty
82 bunny
83 sleeps
   Jill
84 **Field**
   nothing
   faster
85 **grocery**
86 —
87 story
88 —
89 —
90 —
91 —
92 Nancy
93 feeds
   squirrels
   nuts
94 —
95 give
   Ellen
96 wind
   puff

97 —
98 any
99 —
100 —
101 merry-go-
   round
   round
102 —
103 slower
104 —
105 —
106 —
107 —
108 —

UNIT IV

109 —
110 **pasture**
111 —
112 Bill
113 —
114 roosters
115 **orchard**
116 —
117 —
118 —
119 —
120 poky
   galloping
121 met
122 —
123 apple
   trees

124 peep
   robins
   nest
125 birds
126 once
   swish
127 buy
   wee
128 —
129 **machine**
130 baskets
131 —
132 pennies
133 —
134 wagon
135 corn
136 —
137 which
138 —
139 Valentine
140 —
141 —
142 —
143 —
144 —
145 —
146 —
147 woman
148 —
149 fat
150 —
151 —
152 —
153 —

CONTRIBUTIONS TO UNDERSTANDINGS AND BEHAVIOR TRAITS

In guiding the social development of children we are concerned with two aspects of growth. On the one hand we must consider desirable patterns of acting and reacting in democratic group living. On the other hand we must give attention to the understandings out of which desirable attitudes and behavior traits grow.

Hello, David[1] and its accompanying guidebook present learning experiences designed to help children move from dependence on others toward independence in solving problems involved in group living. This program contributes to children's social growth in moving from absorption in self toward concern for and service to others. It promotes appreciation of the interrelationship of individuals in family, neighborhood, school and community groups, and guides children in carrying their share of responsibility in such groups.

The stories provide a springboard for discussion, dramatic play, and other learning activities that contribute to significant understandings and behavior traits. Children find it easy to identify themselves with David and his friends who meet and solve problems similar to those children of this age meet from day to day.

The first unit centers attention on David's activities in a one-room country school located in a typical farming community. In the next unit David and his family move to a new farm. From the new farm David goes by bus to the new school in the city. Here he meets new problems involved in adjusting to a large city school and to new school friends. Unit Three focuses on the large city community in which David's school is located and the adjustments this kind of environment requires. In Unit Four David gains new insights into his farm environment as he sees it through his new friends' eyes.

---

[1] Other books in this program are *Tom and Susan* (Primer), *Peter's Family, Someday Soon, New Centerville,* and *Cross-Country,* published by Scott, Foresman and Company.

UNDERSTANDINGS	BEHAVIOR TRAITS
UNIT ONE—David at the Country School (pp. 6-36)	
The large amount of land needed for pastures and fields means only a few families may live in a farming community.	
Country children have different problems getting to school on time.	Helping a friend to get to school on time.
There are times when good-natured teasing is fun, but it can be carried too far.	Coming to the rescue of a playmate when playfulness has gone too far.
A country school is smaller than a city school. In a country school children of different ages live and work together like a big family.	Helping younger children in school as at home. Giving instant obedience in time of crisis.
A pet deserves sympathetic understanding.	Appreciating humor of a situation.
In a country school the teacher builds the fire, sweeps and cleans, but children can help her in many ways.	Sharing responsibilities in the work of the school with the teacher.
Alertness to group needs usually brings opportunity and recognition.	Recognizing the futility of envy. Sensing what needs doing and doing it cheerfully.
Parents are a real part of school life. Families come together as a community family.	
Parents sometimes move from one community to another.	Adjusting to new conditions without complaining.
It is natural for a family moving to a new community to feel sad at leaving old friends.	Doing thoughtful things to make partings easier—by planning reunions, by making gifts.

UNDERSTANDINGS

UNIT TWO—David at the City School (pp. 37-74)

Uncertainty in the face of the unfamiliar is natural, but fear of the unknown usually proves to be groundless. New benefits often appear in a new situation, as well as new problems which require adjustment.

New children in a neighborhood or in a school often feel insecure. They need friendliness on the part of the children in the neighborhood or school.

City schools often have many more children than country schools. A city school often has many classrooms, and, in addition, such extra rooms as an auditorium or cafeteria. A city school usually has a number of teachers and other workers. The complexity of a city school often makes it seem unfriendly.

Some rudeness must be expected in life.

"Finders, keepers" is not a good practice to follow.

Private property, such as lawns, flowers, fruit owned by neighbors, should be respected. If unintentional damage has been done to a neighbor's property by a group, the group can through discussion determine ways of righting the wrong.

BEHAVIOR TRAITS

Adapting to a new situation by trying a courageous approach and by actively looking for good things in the new situation.

Sensing the insecurity in other people, and helping them to feel at home; for example, by welcoming new children in a school and making them feel a part of their new class.

Practicing courtesy and friendliness in a city school, by such actions as giving new pupils pleasant, helpful directions in finding their way about.

Learning to ignore the occasional rudeness or unfriendliness, and learning to evaluate criticism for what it is worth.

Turning in lost articles to school "Lost and Found" room.

Learning to discuss, decide on and carry out solutions to group problems.

UNDERSTANDINGS

BEHAVIOR TRAITS

UNIT THREE—In the City Neighborhood (pp. 75-108)

Cities are usually composed of a number of different neighborhoods. In addition there is usually a business district downtown where stores of various sorts are concentrated. There may also be a factory district.

Various forms of transportation are used to get from one part of the city to another. The safety of all necessitates traffic rules and regulations.

Learning to abide by safety rules in crossing streets at stoplights and at other intersections; learning to abide by safety regulations on different forms of transportation.

Successful class trips require careful planning.

Participating in the planning of a group project.

Cities provide such places as parks, zoos, swimming pools, for the enjoyment of all the citizens. Rules make possible greater enjoyment of these facilities.

Cooperating in the effort to make public parks and other recreational facilities places which everyone can continue to enjoy.

Unhappy people, children included, sometimes show their unhappiness by being mean or selfish. Such behavior usually causes them to be disliked, and this increases their misery. Such people can be helped to see how their behavior loses them friends.

Helping difficult classmates to learn to take turns, share toys, and in other ways to become part of the group.

Different people can do different things to contribute to the enjoyment of a group.

Respecting each person's contribution.

The school janitor does many things for teachers and children to make school a pleasanter place. In turn children can make his work easier.

Learning to make school a pleasanter place by picking up trash in the schoolroom and on the playground, and by taking care of equipment.

UNDERSTANDINGS

BEHAVIOR TRAITS

Children who live on a farm work along with their fathers and mothers on the essential work of the farm.

Willingness to do work that contributes to family income.

Guests mean additional work for the whole household.

Doing cheerfully the extra work involved in having guests.

There are many opportunities for fun on the farm.

Enjoying the kind of fun one can have at home rather than envying others.

Self-improvement to win group approval is desirable. But popularity is not more desirable than high standards.

Working at a new kind of activity to do it better without lowering standards.

Farm life usually provides a healthful natural environment, plenty of food and opportunities to observe and learn from nature.

Using opportunities to observe and learn from nature.

Farm producers and city consumers are interdependent.

Appreciating the interdependence of farm and city.

The farm is a family enterprise that calls for skill and industry in all its members.

Improving skills needed for better work.

Farm skills are important for all of us.

Recognizing the importance of skills other than the ones you possess.

Faithful work is necessary to reap the benefits of farm life.

Doing faithfully work that needs to be done.

Farm animals are producers of income.

Animals should be treated as useful workers.

A farmer needs and uses many kinds of machinery.

Taking care of equipment.